Contents

Party 1

Holidays 5

Transport 9

Food and Drink 13

Day Trip 17

Shopping 21

Jobs 25

Going Out 29

Decorating 33

Gardening 37

City Planning 41

Paying Bills 45

In the News 48

Health and Fitness 51

Car Boot Sale 55

Banking 59

Published by Coordination Group Publications Ltd.

Editors:
Katie Braid, Rosie Gillham, David Ryan, Dawn Wright.

Contributors:
Peter Hall, Helen Waugh.

Proofreading:
Sarah Blackwood, Helena Hayes and Mark Moody.

ISBN: 978 1 84762 517 5

Images on front cover supplied courtesy of Stagecoach Group.

Groovy website: www.cgpbooks.co.uk

Printed by Elanders Ltd, Newcastle upon Tyne.
Jolly bits of clipart from CORELDRAW®

Based on the classic CGP style created by Richard Parsons.

Party

Q1 Jess is organising a party. Some of her guests have special diets.
She has made a table to show how many meals for special diets she will have to order.

	Vegetarian	Vegan	Gluten-free	Nut allergy	No special diet
Dewi					•
Jenny					•
Simon				•	
Betsy			•		
Miles	•				
Flora			•		
Ieuan					•
Stuart		•			

a) How many of Jess' guests follow a **special diet**?

b) Each meal for a **special diet** will cost **£9**. How much will these meals cost Jess in **total**?

Q2 Jess has bought **3 bottles** of FizzPop and some plastic cups for her party.

FizzPop
1.5 litres

FizzPop
1.5 litres

FizzPop
1.5 litres

Each cup
holds 500 ml

1 litre = 1000 ml

a) How many **litres** of FizzPop has Jess bought?

b) How much FizzPop has Jess bought in **ml**?

c) How many **cups** of FizzPop will Jess be able to pour out?

Party

Q3 Rupert is expecting **10 people** to be at his party. He has worked out how much food he needs to buy **per person** and goes to the shop to buy the things that he needs.

> For each person
> - 4 slices of pizza
> - 25 g of crisps

Delish Pizza
8 slices

a) How many **slices of pizza** does he need?

b) How many **pizzas** does he need to buy?

c) How many **packets of crisps** does he need to buy?

Q4 Jill cooks pizzas at her party. She has **four pizzas** but her oven can only fit **two at a time**. The cooking instructions are shown below.

Squirrel pizza
Oven Temp: 180 °C
Cooking Time: 20 mins

Potato pizza
Cooking temperature: 180 °C
Cooking time: 15 mins

Ham and Peanut Pizza
Cook for 10 mins at 180 °C

Cabbage Pizza
Cook at... 180 °C
Cook for... 15 mins

a) Jill puts the **ham and peanut** pizza and the **squirrel** pizza in the oven at **10:10 pm**. What time should she take them out?

b) As soon as there's space in the oven she puts the **potato** pizza in. What time is this pizza due out?

c) The **cabbage** pizza is the last to go in. What's the **earliest** time it could be ready by?

Party

Q5 Adil's friends planned a mini-sports tournament for his birthday BBQ.
They split into **three teams** and played three games.

Rules!!!
<u>In each game:</u>
10 points for winning
5 points for second place
2 points for last place.

	Game 1	Game 2	Game 3	Total
Team 1	5			
Team 2	2			
Team 3	10			

a) In the second game, **Team 2 won**, **Team 1** came **second** and **Team 3** came **last**.
Copy and complete the table to show these results.

b) **Team 1 won** game 3, with **Team 2** coming **second** and **Team 3 last**.
Add these scores to your table.

c) **Complete** the table to show the **overall results** of the tournament. Which team **won?**

Q6 Mark is organising a party game. He wants to split his guests into teams
based on their **weights**. He asks his guests what their weights are.

	Weight
Nick	68 kg
Simon	13 st 8 pounds
Joe	10 st 3 pounds
Tim	88 kg

1 kg = 2.2 pounds

1 st = 14 pounds

a) Tim and Nick only know their weight in kg. What do they each weigh in **pounds**?
Give your answers to the **nearest pound**.

b) What are Simon and Joe's weights in **pounds**?

Party

Q7   Sally is making 12 party bags. Each bag must contain the same number of chocolate bars and the same number of rubber animals.

Snack Size Chocs
(32 bars)
£2.30

Rubber Animals

90 pieces

a)   What is the **highest** number of **chocolate bars** she can put in each bag?

b)   What is the **highest** number of **rubber animals** she can put in each bag?

c)   Sally's mum finds that **9** of the rubber animals are faulty and throws them away. How many animals can she **now** put in each party bag?

Q8   Chris has made cakes of different flavours for his party.
He mixes the cakes up and offers one to Ken.

Lemon flavoured

Vanilla flavoured

Fish sauce flavoured

a)   What is the probability that Ken will pick a **lemon flavoured** cake?

b)   What is the probability that Ken will **not** pick a **fish sauce flavoured** cake?

Holidays

Q1 Lola is planning a snowboarding trip to Val d'Essert.
She wants to go when there will be the **most snow**.

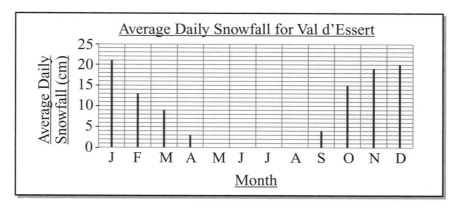

a) In which **month** does Val d'Essert have the highest snowfall?

b) Lola can get a discount if she goes in **October**.
What is the average daily snowfall in October?

Q2 Lola has saved **£600** for her trip.
She has made a list of all the things she needs to pay for.

Snowboarding Costs:

Return Flights: £245.00

Hotel: £164.00

Insurance: £52.50

Train to and from airport: £43.50

a) How much money does Lola need **in total**?

b) How much will she have **left over** for spending money on her trip?

c) Lola's dad offers to **drive** her to and from the airport so she doesn't need to buy train tickets. How much **spending money** will she have now?

Holidays

Q3 Will wants to hire a log cabin for a weekend with his friends. There will be **6 people** in total, and they want to stay for **two nights** (Friday and Saturday) in **May**.

Prices Per Cabin Per Night	Elm Cabin (sleeps 2)	Ash Cabin (sleeps 4)	Oak Cabin (sleeps 6)
Jan-May & Sept-Nov (Mon-Thurs)	£70	£100	£120
Jan-May & Sept-Nov (Fri-Sun)	£95	£125	£150
June-Aug & Dec (Mon-Sun)	£180	£200	£220

a) How much will it cost **in total** to hire a big enough cabin for the two nights?

b) How much will it cost **per person** to hire the cabin if they split the cost equally?

Q4 The cabin is near Travistown. Will and his friends plan to travel to Travistown by train. The owner of the cabin has offered to pick them up from Travistown train station:

From: <u>Mike</u>
To: <u>Will</u>
Subject: Re: Getting to the cabin

Hi Will
I can pick you up from Travistown Station, but it will have to be **before 9pm** on Friday evening. What time does your train get in?
Thanks, Mike.

Out: 17th May
Wrigly (WRI) to Travistown (TRT)

Depart:	1542	1735	1920	2015
Arrive:	1816	1903	2052	2140
Duration:	2h 34m	1h 28m	1h 32m	1h 25m

a) What is the **latest train** leaving from Wrigly that Will and his friends can catch?

b) Will thinks they should get a train that leaves Wrigly **between 5 and 6 pm**. What time should he ask Mike to meet them in Travistown?

c) Will gets home from work at **3.30 pm**. He lives **15 minutes** away from Wrigly station. How much time will he have to pack on the Friday afternoon?

Holidays

Q5 Phillippa and her friends are deciding when to go on holiday to France.
They would like to go when the average midday temperature is **at least 20 °C**
and when there's the **least chance of rain**.

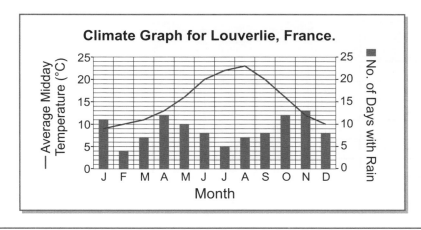

a) Which months have the right **temperature** for Phillippa and her friends?

b) Which month should they plan their holiday for?

Q6 Fiona is looking at a website which shows the price of flights between any two places.
She wants to fly from Manchester to Berlin on the **11th June**,
spending **7 nights** in Berlin before flying back.

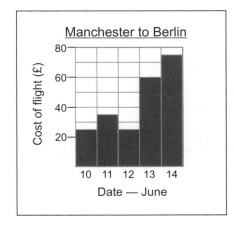
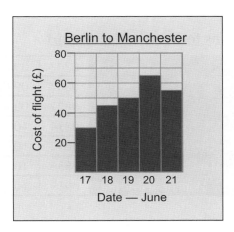

a) How much money will Fiona have to pay for the two flights?

b) The website says there is an extra charge of **£15.75** for tax, and **£11.50** for luggage.
What will the **total cost** of the flights be?

Holidays

Q7 Mr and Mrs Brown and their two children want to go on holiday next year.
They want to go for **one week in June**.
The table below shows combined prices for the flights and hotel.

Number of Nights:	7		14	
Board:	Half	Full	Half	Full
01 Jan — 19 Mar	140	190	200	290
20 Mar — 21 May	180	240	250	330
22 May — 02 July	270	300	360	450
03 July — 10 Sep	330	400	520	630
11 Sep — 26 Nov	230	270	310	420
27 Nov — 31 Dec	270	310	380	470

Prices shown are in **£s per adult**. Child prices are **half** the adult price.

a) How much will it cost for the family to go **half board**?

b) The Browns have a budget of **£950**. Can they afford to go **full board**?

Q8 The Brown family are getting the train from Chorley to Manchester Airport for their flight.
It takes **15 minutes** to walk to Chorley station from the Browns' house,
and they will need **5 minutes** to pick up their tickets at the station.

Trains to Manchester Airport

Lancaster	0747	0926	—	1126
Preston	0807	0945	1004	1145
Chorley	0822	0956	1022	1156
Bolton	0834	1008	1034	1208
Manchester Oxford Road	0852	1023	1052	1223
Manchester Piccadilly	0856	1027	1056	1227
Manchester Airport	0919	1047	1117	1247

Flight Details
Flight No.: BNT3891

Departure Time: 1300

Please arrive no later than 45 mins before departure

a) What is the **latest time** the Browns can arrive at the airport for their flight?

b) What is the **latest time** they can set off from home on the day of their flight?

Transport

Q1 Sophie has to drive a lot as part of her job. Her boss gives her money for petrol. Sophie keeps a record of **how far** she has driven.

Week starting: 15/11/10

Mon — 30 miles

Wed — 28 miles

Thur — 40 miles

Travel Costs
22p will be paid for every mile driven.

a) How many **miles** did Sophie travel in the week starting 15/11/10?

b) How much **money** should Sophie get from her boss to pay for her petrol?

Q2 Mark and Rose live in Newcastle. They are going to London for a holiday. They are trying to work out if it's cheaper to **fly** to London or get the **train**.

Train
Return ticket:
£98 per person.

Fly Rapido
Outbound: £29.99
Inbound: £34.99
(per passenger)

a) How much would it cost Mark and Rose to **both fly** to London and back?

b) Is it **cheaper** for Mark and Rose to **fly** to London or to get the **train**?

10

Transport

Q3 Colin has a job interview in Preston at **11 am**.
The interview is a **15 minute walk** from the bus station.

Bus Timetable							
Westworth	09.23	09.38	09.53	10.08	10.23	10.38
Sterne	09.29	09.44	09.59	10.14	10.29	10.44
Horton	09.45	10.00	10.15	10.30	10.45	11.00
Preston bus station	09.55	10.10	10.25	10.40	10.55	11.10

a) Colin plans to get the **09:53** bus from **Westworth**. What time will he get to the **interview**?

b) Colin misses the 09:53 bus and has to get the **next** one.
Will he still be **in time** for his interview?

Q4 Simon is going to visit his friend Tim in **Furly**.
He looks at a map to work out how far away Tim lives.

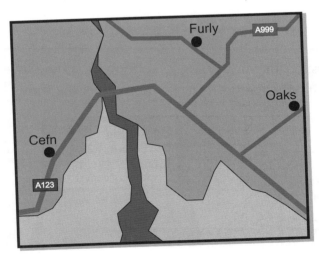

Scale 1 cm : 4 miles

a) Simon lives in **Oaks**. How many **miles** will he have to drive to get to Tim's?

b) Simon and Tim decide to drive from **Tim's house** to **Cefn**.
How many miles is this journey?

Transport

Q5 Caroline wants to visit a friend who lives on the Isle of Man.
She will leave on Friday evening and come back on Sunday afternoon.
She can either get a **flight** or a **ferry** from Liverpool.

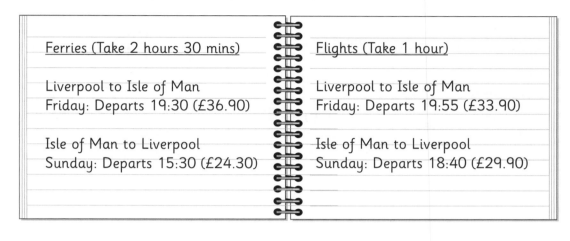

Ferries (Take 2 hours 30 mins)

Liverpool to Isle of Man
Friday: Departs 19:30 (£36.90)

Isle of Man to Liverpool
Sunday: Departs 15:30 (£24.30)

Flights (Take 1 hour)

Liverpool to Isle of Man
Friday: Departs 19:55 (£33.90)

Isle of Man to Liverpool
Sunday: Departs 18:40 (£29.90)

a) What is the **earliest** time on Friday evening that Caroline could arrive on the Isle of Man?

b) Caroline wants her journey to be as **cheap as possible**.
Should she travel by **plane** or **ferry**?

Q6 Richie is working out which service stations he could stop at on the way to visit a friend.
He wants to know the **distances** between some of the service stations.

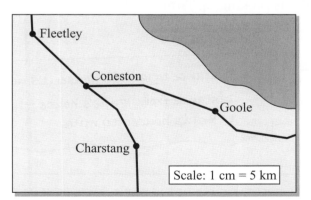

Fleetley

Coneston

Goole

Charstang

Scale: 1 cm = 5 km

1 km ≈ 0.6 miles

a) What is the distance between **Fleetley** and **Goole** in **km**?

b) What is this distance in **miles**?

But it looked like a road on the map...

Transport

Q7   Phil is driving to France for a holiday.
He has written down the different stages of his journey.

<u>Stage 1:</u>
Drive to Folkestone (150 miles)

<u>Stage 2:</u>
Go through the tunnel (takes about 30 mins)

<u>Stage 3:</u>
Drive to the hotel (takes about 30 mins)

CHECK YOUR TIME ZONES

ENGLAND   FRANCE

a)   Phil thinks he will drive at an average of **50 miles per hour**.
How long will it take him to drive to **Folkestone**?

b)   How long will the **whole journey** take him?

c)   Phil sets off at **4 pm English time**. What time will it be in **France** when he arrives?

Q8   Phyllis is driving to the beach. She is picking up Jamie and then Brad on the way.

Likely average speed = 30 mph

Distance to Jamie's house: 15 miles
Distance from Jamie's house
to Brad's house: 10 miles

a)   How long will it take Phyllis to get to **Jamie's** house?

b)   If she leaves Jamie's house at **10 am**, what **time** will she get to **Brad's** house?

Food and Drink

Q1 Chris is cooking a pie in his microwave to eat while watching a film on TV.
The film starts at 7.30 pm.

Power:	Cook For	Stand For	Then Cook For
500 W	4½ mins	1 min	2½ mins
700 W	4 mins	1 min	2 mins
900 W	3½ mins	1 min	1½ mins

a) Chris has a **900 W** microwave. How long **in total** will the pie take to prepare?

b) **What time** should he start to cook it, so that it is ready at exactly 7.30 pm?

Q2 Chloe is cooking Sunday dinner.
She wants the meal to be ready at **1.30 pm**.
To help plan the cooking, she has made these notes.

> **Cooking times...**
>
> <u>Potatoes</u>:
>   Need 20 mins in saucepan then 50 mins in oven.
> <u>Turkey</u>:
>   Cook for 40 mins per kg.
>   Allow to stand for 10 minutes before serving.
>
> <u>Don't forget</u> — Potatoes need peeling!
>   Should take 10 mins.

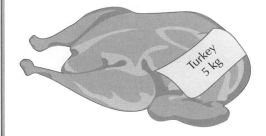

a) How long does the turkey need to be **cooked** for?
Give your answer in hours and minutes.

b) **What time** should Chloe start to cook the turkey, so that it's ready at 1.30 pm?

c) How long **in total** do the potatoes take to **prepare and cook**?

d) What is the **latest time** that Chloe could start peeling
the potatoes so that they are ready to eat at 1.30 pm?

Food and Drink

Q3 Laura has found an old recipe for a cake she wants to bake.
Her electronic scales and measuring jug only show **metric units**.

Ye Olde Cake Recipe
1 lb butter
1½ lb sugar
2 lb flour
6 eggs
½ pint milk
Set oven to 330 °F...

Laura,
1 lb is about 450 g
1 pint is about 570 ml

To change temperatures from °F to °C, use this rule:
"Take away 30 then divide by 2"

Hope this helps! Love from Gran x

a) Work out the amounts of **butter**, **sugar** and **flour** Laura needs in **grams**.

b) How much milk does she need in **ml**?

c) Laura's oven is marked in **°C**. What temperature should she set it to?

Q4 Laura wants to bake some fairy cakes for her friends.
She wants to make **12 cakes** using the recipe shown.

Fairy Cakes
(Makes 36)

375 g butter
750 g sugar
600 g flour
6 eggs
360 ml milk

Work out the amounts of all the ingredients
Laura needs to make **12 cakes**.

Food and Drink

Q5 Andy is making a small fruit cake. He needs 6½ oz flour and 4½ oz brown sugar.
He weighs the flour out in a bowl and starts adding sugar to the same bowl.

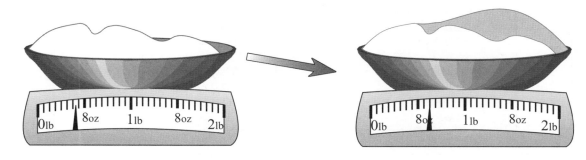

a) Has Andy added the right amount of sugar or does he need more? If so, how much?

b) Andy also needs to weigh out 5½ oz of butter. What should the scale read
with the right amounts of flour, sugar and butter in the bowl **together**?

Q6 Jo is measuring out ingredients to make Carrot and Lentil Soup using weighing
scales and a jug. Her scales come with **one each** of the following weights:

200 g, 100 g, 50 g, 20 g, 5 g and **1 g.**

A

100 g

200 g

Carrot and Lentil Soup
600 g carrots
170 g lentils
150 ml milk

B

200

100

ml

a) What combination of weights should Jo use on her scales to weigh out the **lentils**?

b) Jo has put four carrots on the scales, as shown in diagram A above.
Roughly **how many more carrots** will she need to make the soup?

c) Jo empties the milk from an open bottle into her measuring jug, as shown in diagram B.
How much more milk does she need to add to the jug?

Food and Drink

Q7 Jake is throwing a party. There will be 24 people there. He wants to make enough sausage rolls and cheesy biscuits to serve all 24 people.

> Sausage Rolls
> (serves 12)
>
> 600 g sausage meat
> 1 small onion
> 450 g pastry
> 1 egg

> Cheesy Biscuits
> (serves 8)
>
> 100 g flour
> 100 g butter
> 100 g cheese
> 1 egg

a) How many **onions** does Jake need?

b) How many **eggs** does Jake need?

c) Jake finds 200 g of cheese in the fridge. **How much more** does he need to buy?

Q8 Jake would like to serve fruit punch at the party. He asks his grandma for her special secret recipe:

> Fruit Punch —
> (makes 5 litres)
>
> 2 litres orange juice
> 3 litres ginger ale
>
> Mix together the ingredients in a large cauldron by the light of a full moon.

a) Jake wants to make **10 litres** of punch. How much of each ingredient does he need?

b) Jake only has 3 litres of orange juice. How much **ginger ale** would he need if he used **3 litres** of orange juice to make the punch?

c) Jake changes his grandma's recipe to add **1 litre** of pineapple juice to the orange juice and ginger ale. What quantity of this **new recipe** can he make using **3 litres** of orange juice?

Day Trip

Q1   Mike is visiting Mudley Zoo.
He sees a sign showing the feeding times of different animals.

Daily Feeding Times
Meerkats — 12.00
Sea lions — 10.30 and 15.30
Tigers — 10.30 and 14.30
Polar bears — 11.30
Monkeys — 12.30
Penguins — 16.00
Lions — 15.30

a)   What **order** should Mike visit the animals in, so that he can see them **all** being fed?

b)   Mike wants to stop for a **one hour break** for lunch.
When can he do this **without** missing any feeding times?

Q2   Carly wants to spend a day out at a museum, but isn't sure which one to go to.
She wants to know how much her day out will **cost** at the different museums.

Plane Museum
Ticket Price: £5.20
Transport Costs: £3.90

Police Museum
Ticket Price: £4.50
Transport Costs: £0.60

Postal Museum
Ticket Price: £3.50
Transport Costs: £1.70

Which museum should Carly go to, to make her day as **cheap as possible**?

Day Trip

Q3 | Helen and Nigel drive to a bike hire shop in Helen's car and park in the car park.

WELCOME TO
BIKESTEER HIRE SHOP

◄——— CAR PARK
(£5 ALL DAY)

ENTRANCE ———►

Bike Hire Prices (per day)

Adult Bike: £15

Child Bike: £10

A deposit of £50 per bike is needed.
It will be refunded when the bikes
are returned.

a) Helen pays for the **car park**, **2 adult bikes** and the **deposit**. How much will this cost?

b) Helen and Nigel split the cost of the **parking** and the **bikes equally** between them.
How much does Nigel owe Helen?

Q4 | Helen and Nigel use the map below while they are out on their bike ride.

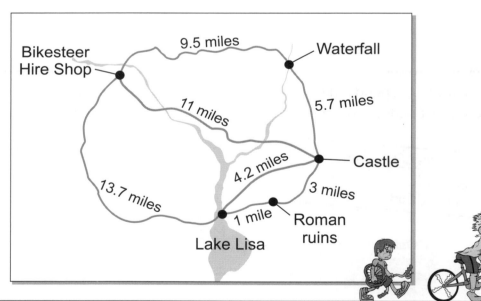

a) Helen and Nigel cycle from **Bikesteer Hire Shop** to the
waterfall and then the **castle**. How many **miles** is this?

b) Helen and Nigel are halfway between the **Roman ruins** and **Lake Lisa** when it starts to
rain. What is the **shortest** route back to **Bikesteer Hire Shop** from where they are now?

Day Trip

Q5 Liam has booked his birthday party at 'Swinging Trees' for **himself** and **5 friends**.
He has hired a **minibus** for the day to take them there and back.

> **Thank you for booking your party at...**
>
> The Swinging Trees High Ropes Adventure Course!
>
> Start time: 11 am
> (please arrive half an hour early for your safety briefing).
>
> Cost per person: £28
>
> Minibus Hire
> for 1 day: £54

a) It takes **45 mins** to get to 'Swinging Trees'. What is the **latest time** they can set off?

b) How much will the minibus cost **per person** if they split it equally?

c) How much will the **whole day** cost each person?

Q6 Mia and Deanne are planning a day in town.
They want to see a **fashion show** at Bedhams and go to the '**Quick Flash Sale**!'
They also want to see '**Snow Age**' at the cinema.
The cinema is 20 minutes away from Bedhams.

> **Bedhams Department Store**
> Fashion Show: 10.00 – 11.00
>   12.30 – 13.30
>
> *Quick Flash Sale!* starts at 15.30

> **Cinema Film Times**
> Snow Age: 11.00 – 13.00
>   11.30 – 13.30
>   14.00 – 16.00
>   14.30 – 16.30

a) Which **fashion show** and **film showing** should the girls go to? Explain your answer.

b) The girls want to have lunch at Bedhams **before** the Quick Flash Sale.
How much time will they have?

Day Trip

Q7 Wayne is planning a trip to a theme park. He looks at the theme park prices online.

SCREEM PARK

Entrance Fee £5.

Rides £3 each.

Ride photos £2 each.

a)   How much would it cost Wayne to go to the park and go on **6 rides**?

b)   Wayne has **£40** to spend. If he goes on **9 rides**, how many **photos** can he buy?

Q8 Betty wants to visit the **War Museum**, **Art Gallery** and **Science Museum**.
Her dad will drop her off and pick her up from the **War Museum**,
and she will travel between each place by **boat**.

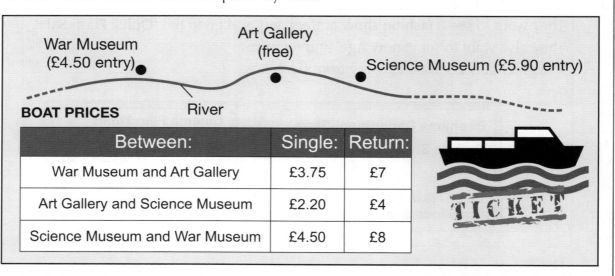

War Museum
(£4.50 entry)

Art Gallery
(free)

Science Museum (£5.90 entry)

BOAT PRICES   River

Between:	Single:	Return:
War Museum and Art Gallery	£3.75	£7
Art Gallery and Science Museum	£2.20	£4
Science Museum and War Museum	£4.50	£8

TICKET

If Betty buys her boat tickets in the cheapest way possible,
what will be the **total cost** of her day trip?

Shopping

Q1 Lynn is in charge of buying oranges and juice for her hockey match this week.
Her captain has left her a message:

Hi Lynn,

Please bring enough oranges so the
11 of us, and the 11 people on the
other team, can have 2 quarters each.

Please also bring half a litre of juice
for each member of our team.

Thanks, Cath

a) How many **orange quarters** should Lynn prepare for **each team**?

b) How many **oranges** should Lynn buy?

c) How many **litres** of juice should Lynn buy?

Q2 The captain of the hockey team, Cath, wants to order some new
team shirts from her local sports shop. She has a budget of **£200**.

Hockey Shirt
(no logo)
£15 each

Hockey Shirt
(with team logo)
£20 each

a) How much will it cost for 11 shirts **without** a logo?

b) Can Cath afford to buy 11 shirts **with** a logo?

c) The sports shop offer her a **20% discount** on the shirts with logos.
How much will it cost for the 11 shirts with the discount?

Shopping

Q3 Emma has bought some food from the grocers.
She checks her receipt because she thinks she has been **overcharged**.

```
chicken breasts
   2 @ £3.80 = £7.60
sandwich £2.20
crisps 45p
juice 60p
```

a) The sandwich, crisps and juice Emma bought were on a **£3 meal deal**.
How much has she been **overcharged** for these items?

b) The chicken breasts were on a '**buy one get one half price**' offer.
How much should Emma have been charged for the two chicken breasts?

c) How much should Emma get as a refund from the cashier?

Q4 The owner of the shop gives Emma some vouchers to apologise for her being overcharged. The items Emma buys on her next shop are shown below:

```
bread £1.20
milk 80p
pasta £1.30
tea bags £2.40
cereal £2.20
```

How much will Emma **save** in total if she uses all the vouchers?

Shopping

Q5 John is doing some online shopping and has found 3 DVDs he wants to buy.
He has a choice of two companies to buy from:

MooveeWorld:

All DVDs
£12 each!

Free P&P on orders over £30

Films4everyone:

DVDs
£13 each or 3 for £30
P&P £4.50 to any UK address

a) How much would John pay for his DVDs from **MooveeWorld**?

b) How much **cheaper** would it be for John to get the DVDs from Fims4everyone?

c) John remembers he has a voucher from MooveeWorld which gives him **10% off** his order.
Will it now be cheaper to get the DVDs from MooveeWorld or from Films4everyone?

Q6 Alison wants to buy the pair of shoes shown below. If she opens a store card,
she could buy the shoes today and pay for them **plus interest** in one month's time.

£70

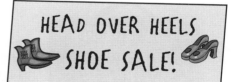

HEAD OVER HEELS
SHOE SALE!

5% off any purchase today

OR

open a store card* and
get **10% OFF** the price
shown on the ticket.

*Interest charged at 5% per month.

a) What price will the shoes be if Alison opens a store card?

b) How much will Alison have to pay in **one month's time** if she opens a store card?

c) Is it cheaper for Alison to open a store card, or pay for the shoes today?

Shopping

Q7 Jenny is going on holiday. Her neighbour Pete has offered to look after her two dogs. Every day, each dog eats $\frac{3}{4}$ tin of dog food and 250 g of mixer.

DOG FOOD

TINS each
£1.24

MIXER

10 kg bag
£25.80

a) How much dog food and mixer should Jenny tell Pete to buy to feed the dogs for **2 weeks**?

b) How much **money** should Jenny give to Pete to buy the food?

Q8 Paul is trying to work out which washing detergent to buy.
The choices are:

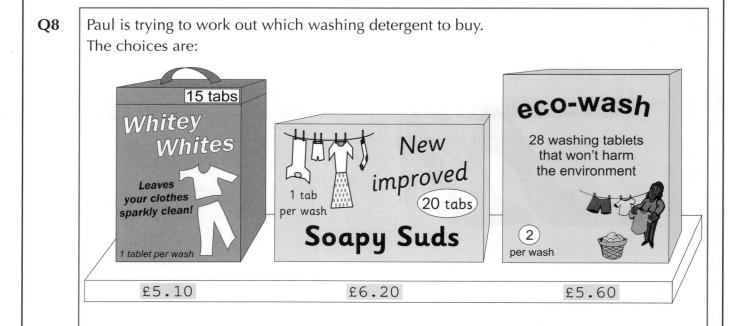

15 tabs

Whitey Whites

Leaves your clothes sparkly clean!

1 tablet per wash

New improved

1 tab per wash

20 tabs

Soapy Suds

eco-wash

28 washing tablets that won't harm the environment

2 per wash

£5.10   £6.20   £5.60

Which detergent is the **best value for money**?

Jobs

Q1 Josh works in a fish & chip shop. He earns **£5.50 an hour**.
He writes down when he will be working this week in his diary.

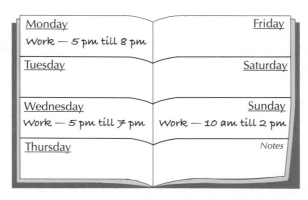

Monday	Friday
Work — 5 pm till 8 pm	
Tuesday	Saturday
Wednesday	Sunday
Work — 5 pm till 7 pm	Work — 10 am till 2 pm
Thursday	Notes

a) How many **hours** will Josh work this week?

b) How much will Josh get **paid** this week?

Q2 Phil is looking for a job. He visits a recruitment agency to find
information about the different jobs that are available.

Work	Shifts per week	Length of shift
Office work	6	4 hours
Factory work	3	12 hours

Office work: £4.50 per hour
Factory work: £6.00 per hour

a) How much would Phil get paid each **week** if he took a job in an **office**?

b) How much **more** would Phil get paid each **week** if he took a job in a **factory**?

Jobs

Q3 Ben and Charlie see an advert for a paper round in a newsagent's window.

> **Paper Rounds**
> We are looking for a reliable
> person to do a paper round 7 days a week.
> This job could be split between two people.
> <u>Pay is £56 per week.</u>

a) How much does the newsagent pay for **each round** of papers that are delivered?

b) Ben and Charlie get the job and split the paper round. Ben delivers papers on **Mondays** and **Wednesdays**. Charlie does it on the other days. How much will they **each** get paid?

Q4 Polly is starting a company that organises holidays for big groups in a country house. She is working out how much money it will cost her to set up each holiday.

Things I'll have to pay for...
Hiring the country manor
(£2500 for a week)

Hiring a chef
(£300 for a week)

Hiring a cleaner for
the end of the week (£60)

a) How much will it cost Polly to organise a **week long holiday** for a group?

b) Polly wants to make a **£260 profit** on each holiday.
How much should she charge a group for a week long holiday?

c) A group of **15 people** book a week long holiday with Polly's company.
They want to pay **per person**. How much should Polly charge **each person**?

Jobs

Q5 Kelly thinks she'd like a career in science.
She looks up some jobs advertised online to see what the salaries are.

Science Job	Salaries		
Biologist	£30 000	£28 000	£32 000
Chemist	£34 000	£52 000	£25 000
Physicist	£48 000	£28 000	£30 000

a) Which job has the highest **mean salary**?

b) Which job has the smallest **range** of salaries?

Q6 Jenny is looking for a new job. She sees adverts for two different jobs.

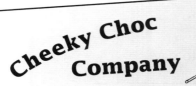

Cheeky Choc Company

Position: Sales Representative
Salary: £12 000 per year
PLUS 15% yearly bonus
(if all targets met)

Fizgig Fashions

Position: Sales Representative
Salary: £13 000 per year
PLUS 10% yearly bonus
(if all sales targets are met)

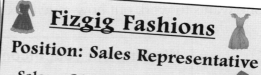

a) How much would Jenny get paid each year, **in total**, if she worked for the Cheeky Choc Company and met all her targets?

b) How much **more** could she get paid each year working if she worked for Fizgig Fashions and met all her sales targets?

Jobs

Q7 Elaine works **part time** as a music teacher.

She has kept a record of how many lessons she has taught **each week** for the last **six** weeks:

Week Beginning:	Number of Lessons:
7th Jan	12
14th Jan	13
21st Jan	11
28th Jan	14
4th Feb	10
11th Feb	18

a) What is the **mean** number of lessons Elaine teaches **each week**?

b) Elaine charges **£10.50** per lesson.
On **average**, how much does she earn from teaching music **each week**?

c) Elaine would like to earn **£10 000 per year**. If she continues teaching the same mean number of lessons each week, can she earn this amount from teaching music?

Q8 Danni is starting a new job as an outdoors instructor.
She will be paid **£16 000** a year.
She wants to work out how much tax she will have to pay.

> **Working out your Income Tax** — _A Helpful Guide_
>
> If you earn less than £37 400:
> You will not be taxed on the first £6475.
> You will be taxed 20% on the rest of your money
>
> _Example:_ if you earn £14 000
> First £6475 is tax free.
> £14 000 – £6475 = £7525
> so 20% of £7525 will be taken out of your wages.

How much income tax will Danni have to pay **each year**?

Going Out

Q1 Dee is meeting her friend Stef in town.

Stef lives **10 minutes' walk** from town, and Dee lives **30 minutes' drive** away.

Dee sends Stef a message as she sets off in a taxi:

a) What time should Dee **arrive in town**?

b) What is the **latest time** Stef can set off from her house to meet Dee on time?

c) After meeting, the girls need to walk to the cinema **15 minutes** away to meet another friend, Kay. What time should they tell Kay they will get there?

Q2 The three girls share a taxi back to Dee's house, and read the cost from the meter:

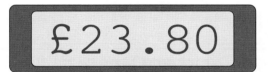

They want to give the driver a tip of **£3**.

a) What is the **total amount** they should pay, including the tip, to the nearest pound?

b) How much should **each girl** pay, if they split the total cost **equally** between them?

c) Each of the girls only has a £10 note.
How much **change** should they each get back after paying the driver?

Going Out

Q3 The Robinson family are going to watch the ballet.
There are **two adults**, an **OAP**, a **student** and a **child** in the group.
They are trying to work out the cheapest way to buy tickets to sit in the **circle**.

Swiss Theatre

What's on: *Duck Pond — The Ballet*

Prices for tonight's show:

	Circle	Stalls
Adult	£30	£35
OAP	£25	£28
Student	£25	£28
Child (under 16)	£15	£17
Group of 5	£135	£155

a) Will it be **cheaper** for the family to buy their tickets separately, or as a 'Group of 5'?

b) Mrs Robinson has two vouchers for 50% off adult tickets.
What is the **lowest amount** the family can pay in total?

Q4 Mr Robinson goes to the theatre bar in the interval to buy drinks for the whole family.

He takes a £20 note with him, and looks at the price list while he queues.

Juice Bar	
St Clements:	£4.30
Cranberry Crush:	£3.95
Tutti Frutti:	£4.40
Passionfruit Punch	£4.25

a) Mr Robinson wants to buy **5 of the same drink**.
Which of the drinks can he afford to buy?

b) Will he have enough money to buy the drinks plus a packet of sweets costing **85p**?

Going Out

Q5 Hannah and Wayne are going to watch the film 'Rare Earth Element' at the cinema on **Minsterbury High Street**. They want to catch the bus from **Nauton Green**.

Hastwick	1605	1705	1805
Nauton Green	1635	1735	1835
Minsterbury Castle St.	1650	1750	1850
Minsterbury High St.	1655	1755	1855
Minsterbury Bus Station	1705	1805	1905

Minsterbury Bus Station	1915	2015	2115*
Minsterbury High St.	1925	2025	2125
Minsterbury Castle St.	1930	2030	2130
Nauton Green	1945	2045	2145
Hastwick	2015	2105	2205

*Last Bus

Film Times:

Rare Earth Element (160 mins*)
Starts: 1800

Snakes on a Coach (150 mins*)
Starts: 1915

Taxidermist (125 mins*)
Starts: 2145

*Plus approx. 20 mins of trailers
at start of the screening.

a) It takes 10 minutes to walk to the bus stop in Nauton Green.
What is the **latest time** Hannah and Wayne can set off to get to the cinema on time?

b) Hannah is worried that they will miss the last bus home after the film.
Will they be in time to catch it or should they try to arrange a lift home?

Q6 At the cinema, Hannah and Wayne are buying popcorn and lemonade.
There are different sizes of each available:

£2.00

£4.50

150 g

Popcorn 50 g

Popcorn 75 g

£1.30

£1.00

£2.25

330 ml   500 ml

a) Which size lemonade gives the best **value for money**?

b) Hannah and Wayne want **75 g** of popcorn each.
What is the **lowest amount** they could spend on the popcorn?

Going Out

Q7 Nick, Dave, Tom and Ross are having pizza in town.
They each want **6 slices of pizza**.

Pizza My Mind Restaurant
Price List

Pizzas (any topping)
Small (6 slices): £5.50
Medium (8 slices): £7.50
Large (12 slices): £9.50

Special Offer Meal Deals:
(Students Only)

1. Two small pizzas: £10

2. Three medium pizzas: £18

a) What is the lowest amount they could pay **without** ordering one of the meal deals?

b) The waitress tells them they can order a **meal deal**.
Which is the cheapest option for the boys to order now?

Q8 After their meal, the four boys ask for the bill. They want to **round up** the total to
the nearest pound, add on a **20% tip**, and split this amount equally between them.

Pizza My Mind Restaurant

You were served by: Jemima

Food — £32.80
Drinks — £4.90

Total amount — £37.70

(Service charge not included)

How much does **each boy** need to pay?

Decorating

Q1 Teresa is painting her living room.
She wants to know how much paint she needs to buy.

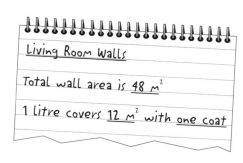

a) How many **litres** of paint does Teresa need to paint the room with **one coat**?

b) How many **litres** of paint does she need to paint the room with **three coats**?

c) How many **tins** should she buy to paint the room with **three coats**?

Q2 Teresa wants to put a wooden skirting board all the way around her living room walls.

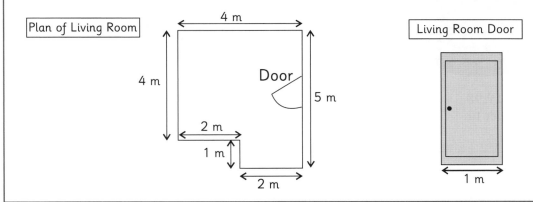

a) What is the **total perimeter** of the room?

b) Theresa needs the skirting board to go all the way around the **walls**, but **not** across the **door**. What length of board should she buy?

Decorating

Q4 Donna wants a glass screen to go above her oven. The D.I.Y. shop has asked Donna to sketch the screen she needs. The shop sells glass by **area**.

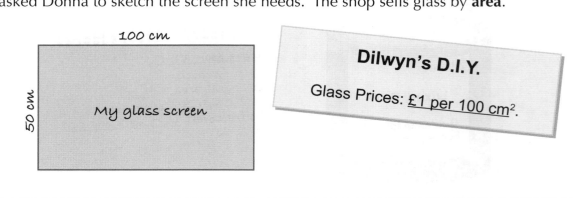

100 cm

50 cm

My glass screen

Dilwyn's D.I.Y.

Glass Prices: £1 per 100 cm².

a) What **area** of glass does Donna need?

b) How much will she have to **pay** for the screen?

Q3 Hayley is decorating her bedroom. She wants to **estimate** how much it will cost her.

Luxury Paint
DUCK EGG BLUE
2 litres

£9.98
per tin

Wallpaper Paste

£4.47
per pack

Border
6 m roll

£8.13
per roll

a) Hayley needs **4 tins** of paint. **Estimate** how much this will cost her.

b) Hayley also wants **2 packs** of **wallpaper paste** and **3 rolls** of the **border**. **Estimate** how much these will cost her in total.

c) **Estimate** the **total cost** of decorating the room.

Decorating

Q5 Daniel wants new carpet tiles for his office. A plan of the room is shown below:

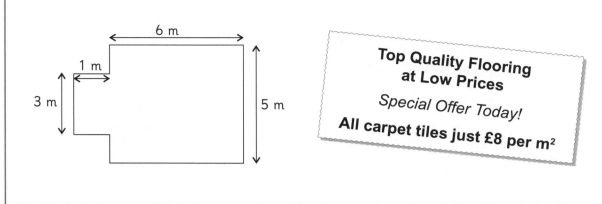

a) What **area** of carpet tiles does Daniel need?

b) How much will it **cost** Daniel to buy carpet tiles for his office?

Q6 Vin wants to tile his bathroom wall with two types of tiles (shown below). He has **20** of each type of tile.

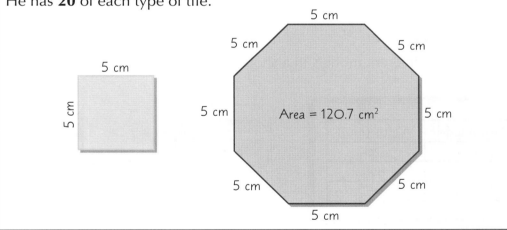

a) Draw a diagram to show how the two types of tiles **fit together**.

b) What is the **total area** of all the **square** tiles?

c) What is the **total area** of all the **octagonal** tiles?

d) What is the **total area** of **all** the tiles? Give your answer to the nearest 100 cm².

Decorating

Q7 James is painting his bathroom light blue.
He needs to mix dark blue paint with white paint to make the right colour.

Painting the bathroom...

Area to paint is 36 m²

Need 0.5 litre of paint per square metre of wall

Mix together blue and white paint in the ratio:

1 : 2

White Paint
2 litres

Dark Blue Paint
2 litres

a) How much **light blue paint** does James need to make?

b) How many **tins** of **white paint** will James need?

Q8 Claire needs a new oven.
She is looking at three different models in a shop.

Oven Model	Width (mm)
SuperHeater	620
OvenSolution	614
HotOven	615

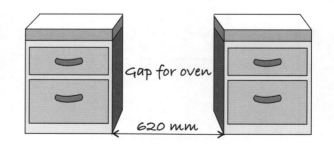

Gap for oven

620 mm

a) The gap for the oven in Claire's kitchen has been measured to the **nearest 10 mm**.
What is the **smallest** it could be?

b) The widths of the ovens are given to the **nearest mm**.
Which of the ovens should Claire buy to be **sure** it will fit?

Gardening

Q1 Jordan is redesigning his garden. He wants to have a lawn and one large flower bed. He will need to order turf for his lawn.

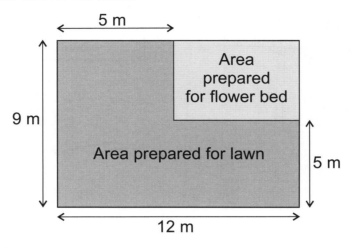

a) What is the **total area** of Jordan's **garden**?

b) What is the **area** of the **flower bed**?

c) What **area** of **turf** will Jordan need to order for his **lawn**?

Q2 Jordan orders **10 rolls** of turf from Turf Shack.

> ### Turf Shack
>
> We sell turf by the roll,
> and deliver <u>anywhere</u> in the UK!
>
> Price per roll: £4.75
>
> <u>Delivery Charges:</u>
>
> Under 10 rolls: £9.25
> 10-20 rolls: £14.25
> Over 20 rolls: £19.25

a) How much will **10 rolls** of turf cost Jordan if he collects them **himself**?

b) How much will **10 rolls** of turf cost Jordan if he has them **delivered**?

Gardening

Q3 Aftab wants to make a patio in his garden. He is going to use concrete slabs.

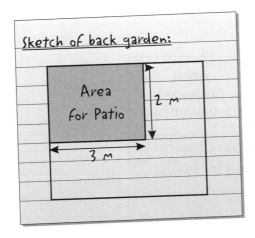

Sketch of back garden:

Area for Patio

2 m

3 m

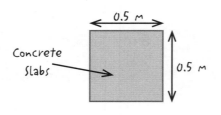

Special Offer on Concrete Slabs
Now just <u>50p</u> per slab!

0.5 m

Concrete Slabs

0.5 m

a) What is the **area** of Aftab's patio?

b) How many **concrete slabs** will he need to buy?

c) How much will it **cost** to buy the slabs?

Q4 Aftab decides to add a border made from wooden blocks all the way around his patio.

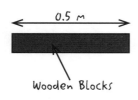

0.5 m

Wooden Blocks

Wooden Blocks
Pack of 15 blocks just £5

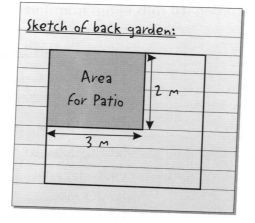

Sketch of back garden:

Area for Patio

2 m

3 m

a) What is the **perimeter** of Aftab's patio?

b) How many **wooden blocks** will he need to buy to make the border?

c) How much will it **cost** to buy enough **packs** of wooden blocks?

Gardening

Q5   Helena has bought some liquid lawn feed to put on her lawn.
She reads the instructions to find out how much to use.

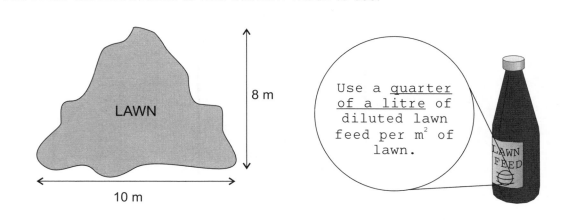

8 m

LAWN

10 m

Use a <u>quarter of a litre</u> of diluted lawn feed per m² of lawn.

a)   **Estimate** the area of Helena's lawn.

b)   How much **diluted** lawn feed does she need to treat the lawn?

Q6   Helena reads the instructions to find out how to dilute the lawn feed.

To use:
Lawn feed must be diluted with water.
For each <u>5 ml</u> of lawn feed add <u>75 ml</u> of water.

Feed me Seymour!

Helena measures out **7.5 litres** of **water** in her watering can.
How much **lawn feed** does she need to add to this?

Gardening

Q7 Sarah is redesigning her garden and has made this sketch of it.

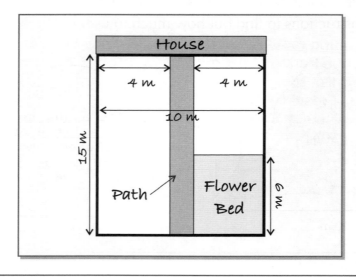

Draw a proper **scale plan** of Sarah's garden, using a scale of **1 cm : 2 m**.

Q8 Harry is building a pond in his garden.
He wants to put a border made of tiles around the pond.

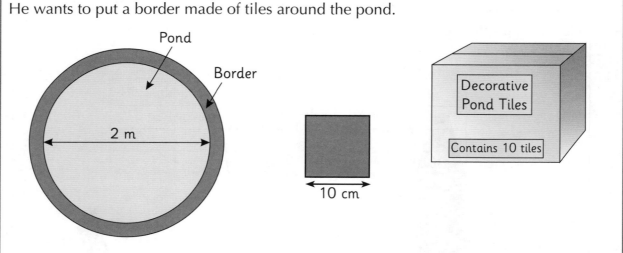

a) What is the perimeter of the pond in **metres**?

b) How many **boxes of tiles** will Harry need to buy to go all the way around the pond?

City Planning

Q1 Jenny is working out the cost of resurfacing roads in Brieston.

Roads needing resurfacing:
Camby to Vue Park — 8.6 miles
Vue Park to Beesdon — 4.7 miles
Beesdon to Freshfall — 11.2 miles
Freshfall to Camby — 6.1 miles

Cost of surfacing the road:
£2000 per mile

a) How many **miles** of road are being resurfaced?

b) How much will it **cost** to **resurface** the roads?

c) Jenny estimates that it will take **2 days** to resurface **each mile** of road. How many days **in total** should the resurfacing take?

Q2 Alex's job is to make sure that there are enough houses being built for the population of Cheddarville. He looks at how the population has changed since 2000.

Year	Population (to the nearest hundred)
2000	43 000
2005	44 800
2010	46 600

a) Describe how the population of Cheddarville **changed** between **2000** and **2005**.

b) Describe how the population of Cheddarville **changed** between **2005** and **2010**.

c) **Predict** what the population of Cheddarville will be in **2020**.

City Planning

Q3 A bypass was built to reduce the number of vehicles driving through Cowton.
A survey was done to see if it was successful.

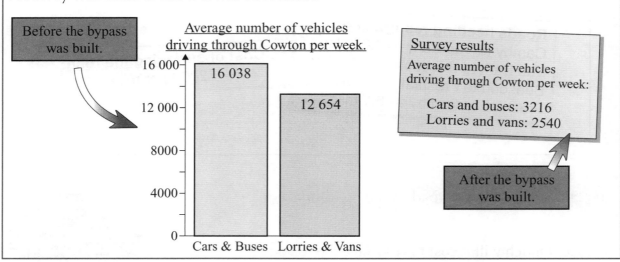

Before the bypass was built.

Average number of vehicles driving through Cowton per week.

Survey results

Average number of vehicles driving through Cowton per week:

Cars and buses: 3216
Lorries and vans: 2540

After the bypass was built.

Cars & Buses   Lorries & Vans

a) How many vehicles drove through Cowton each week **before** the bypass was built?

b) How many **fewer** vehicles drive through Cowton each week now the bypass has been built?

Q4 Planners want to build a bypass near Sheepston so that vehicles do not have to drive through Sheepston town centre.

```
Item no. 3 Sheepston Bypass

The facts: 35 000 vehicles drive through Sheepston each week.

A bypass will reduce this by 80%.

Vehicles will be charged £3 each time they use the bypass.
This will help to pay off the £36 million cost of the bypass.
```

a) How many **fewer** vehicles would drive through Sheepston each week if the bypass was built?

b) How much **money** would be made **each week** by charging vehicles to use the bypass?

c) How **long** will it take for the money charged for using the bypass to pay off the cost of building it?

City Planning

Q5 | Craig is designing an office building. He has drawn **plan views** of two of his ideas.

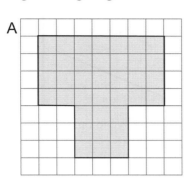 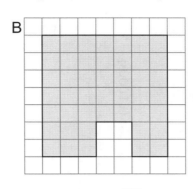

Height of building: 50 m

☐ = 1 m²

a) Work out the **perimeter** of building A and building B.

b) The walls of the building will be made from **glass**.
How much glass would be needed to make each of the buildings?

Q6 | Craig has changed his design and has drawn a sketch of the new office block.
The plans are being shown in the town hall.

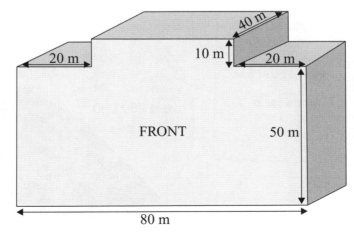

Draw the **front elevation**, **side elevation** and **plan view** of the office block.
Use a scale of **1 cm : 10 m** for each.

City Planning

Q7 The local council is resurfacing a carpark with concrete.

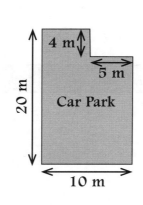

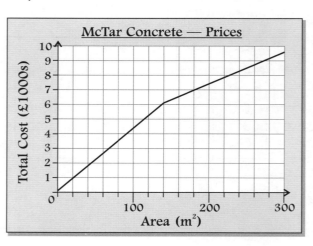

a) What is the **area** of the carpark?

b) What will the **total cost** of the concrete be?

Q8 The New Housing Committee are responsible for making sure there are enough 'low-cost' houses in Cheddarville. Their annual report shows their targets and their results.

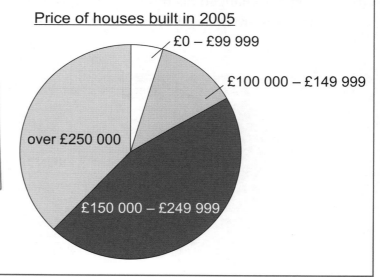

Housing in Cheddarville

2005 Target: 25% of new houses must be 'low-cost'

'Low-cost' houses are houses that cost less than £150 000).

Price of houses built in 2005

£0 – £99 999
£100 000 – £149 999
over £250 000
£150 000 – £249 999

a) Have the New Housing Committee **met** their target? Explain your answer.

b) **1500** new houses are going to be built.
How many of these should be 'low-cost', according to the committee's target?

Paying Bills

Q1 Tim wants to buy solar panels for his house.
The government will give him some money towards the panels.

> *Solar panels — save money AND save the planet!*
>
> Solar panels — **£12 000**.
> Government grant available — up to **£3500**.
> Save **£500 a year** on your energy bills.

a) How much will Tim have to **pay** for the panels, if he gets the full Government grant?

b) How many **years** will it take for the amount he saves on bills
to pay for the cost of the panels?

Q2 Tim pays a fixed rate of **£223 per year** for his water. He would like to install a
water meter, which would mean he only pays for the amount of water he actually uses.

> ### WaterULike Ltd
> Average water usage and cost **per year** with a water meter:
>
> | No. of people in household | Water usage (m³) | Cost (£) |
> |:---:|:---:|:---:|
> | 1 | 54 | 156 |
> | 2 | 108 | 264 |
> | 3 | 142 | 332 |
> | 4 | 167 | 382 |

a) Tim lives alone. How much would he pay on **average** each **month** with the water meter?

b) How much money would he **save each year** with the water meter?

c) Tim's girlfriend moves in with him.
Will it be **cheaper** to have the meter or pay the fixed rate?

Paying Bills

Q3   Lucy is organising her birthday party, and has received the invoice below.
She has already paid a deposit of **£200** and must now pay **half** the remaining amount.

INVOICE: Lucy Jones
Party: 12th June 2011

Venue hire	£250
Buffet meal 50 people @ £12.99 each	£779.40
Total	£1029.40
Less deposit	− £200
	£829.40

Please pay £414.70 by 1st May.

a)   The cost is higher than Lucy was expecting.
How much should she have been charged for the **buffet**?

b)   What is the correct amount that Lucy has to pay by the **1st May**?

Q4   Anna receives a bill based on an **estimate** of how much gas she's used.
She takes a meter reading and discovers she's only used **478** units.

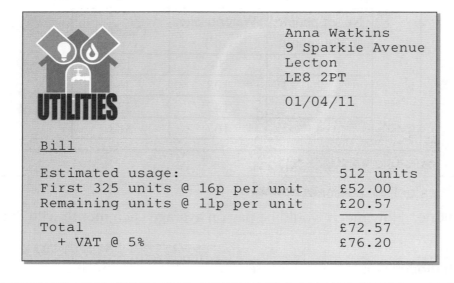

```
UTILITIES                   Anna Watkins
                            9 Sparkie Avenue
                            Lecton
                            LE8 2PT

                            01/04/11

Bill

Estimated usage:                512 units
First 325 units @ 16p per unit  £52.00
Remaining units @ 11p per unit  £20.57

Total                           £72.57
  + VAT @ 5%                     £76.20
```

a)   How much should Anna have to pay **before** VAT is added?

b)   What should the **total cost** of Anna's gas bill be?

Paying Bills

Q5 Tracy bought her car for **£995** one year ago.
The car's value has fallen by **15%** since she bought it.

The car has failed its MOT and needs some repairs.

The garage give Tracy a breakdown of the costs:

PRICE LIST	
Parts:	
Radiator	£155
Brakes	£75
Exhaust	£85
Tyres (set of 4)	£210
Oil service	£35
Labour charge	£95

a) What is the **total cost** of the repairs?

b) Will Tracy have to pay more to fix her car than the car is currently worth?

Q6 Jane wants to try to reduce her mobile phone bill by switching to a different tariff.
Her options are shown below:

Dear Jane
Here is a summary of your mobile phone
usage for September:

Calls: 90 mins
Texts: 130
Total Cost: £34.20

TARIFF		Inclusive calls per month	Inclusive texts per month	Line Rental	Call and Text Charges
	TextyText	30 minutes	250 messages	£14	Calls 15p/min
	TextyTalk	200 minutes	50 messages	£18	Texts 10p/msg

Based on her usage for September, which tariff should Jane choose so she has the **lowest bill** each month?

In the News

Q1   Vikram has written an article for the local paper about giant toads invading the park:

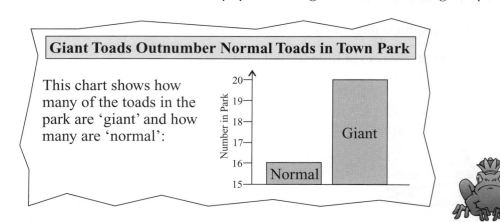

Giant Toads Outnumber Normal Toads in Town Park

This chart shows how many of the toads in the park are 'giant' and how many are 'normal':

a)   How many **giant** toads are there in the park?

b)   How many **normal** toads are there in the park?

c)   Explain why Vikram's bar chart might be **misleading**.

Q2   Ken is a radio reporter covering a match in the National Staring Contest.
In the pre-match build-up he looks at the **past performances** of the contenders.

Contender A: 'Eyes' McGregor
Past Performance:

Opponent	Result	Stare Time (mins to nearest min)
Laura Lashes	Won	42
Max Stare	Lost	13
Carol Cornea	Won	11
Retinal Ryan	Won	88
Mary Myopia	Won	49

Contender B: Arthur 'The Unblinkable'
Past Performance:

Opponent	Result	Stare Time (mins to nearest min)
Carol Cornea	Won	55
Mary Myopia	Won	17
Retinal Ryan	Lost	44
Max Stare	Lost	19
Laura Lashes	Won	45

a)   Which contender has the longest **total stare time** over their previous games?

b)   Based on **past performance**, which contender is most likely to **win**?

In the News

Q3 The Newzcrunch website has a weekly online poll. Courtney is thinking about using the results of the latest poll for a school essay on 'popular culture'.

a) What **percentage** of people who voted said that MDobz were the best?

b) How many **people** said they were the best?

c) Give **two reasons** why the results of the poll might be unreliable.

Q4 Rubi looks in the newspaper at houses for sale in Udderston and Trundle.

Houses in Trundle

3 bed Semi	£120 000
2 bed Terraced	£100 000
1 bed Flat	£95 000
2 bed Terraced	£110 000
2 bed Flat	£98 000

Houses in Udderston

2 bed Flat	£75 000
1 bed Flat	£60 000
3 bed Detached	£160 000
2 bed Terraced	£95 000
3 bed Semi	£155 000

a) What is the **mean** house price in **Trundle**?

b) What is the **mean** house price in **Udderston**?

c) Is there a greater **range** of house prices in Udderston or Trundle?

In the News

Q5 Andrew and Layla are journalists investigating unemployment for their local newspaper. They both carried out **surveys** and gave their results to the editor of the newspaper.

> *Andrew's Unemployment Survey:*
> I stood outside the job centre on Tuesday morning and asked 10 people whether they had a job. <u>90%</u> were unemployed.

> *Layla's Unemployment Survey:*
> I stood in the centre of town on Sunday afternoon and asked 100 people whether they had a job. <u>5%</u> were unemployed.

a) Whose results are the more **reliable**? Give **two reasons** for your answer.

b) There are approximately **20 000** people of working age in the local area.
Based on the more reliable survey result, predict how many of these are **unemployed**.

Q6 Gavin is writing about unemployment in **different areas**.
He finds some pie charts that he wants to use in his article.

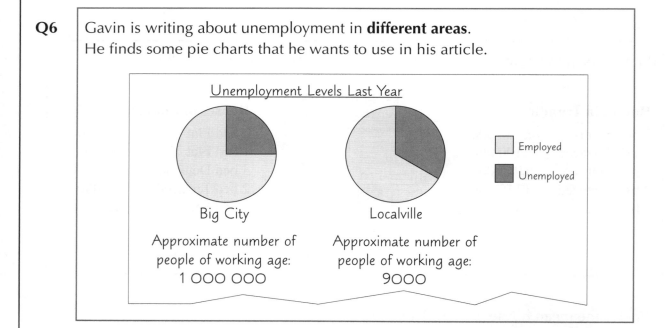

Unemployment Levels Last Year

Big City
Localville

Employed
Unemployed

Approximate number of people of working age:
1 000 000

Approximate number of people of working age:
9000

Approximately how many **people** of working age are unemployed in each area?

Health and Fitness

Q1 Laura wants to join the local leisure centre. The membership prices are shown below.

> **Local Leisure Ltd.**
>
> <u>Membership Prices (per month):</u>
>
> Swimming pool membership — £25
>
> Gym membership — £35
>
> Combined gym and pool membership — £45

a) How much will it cost Laura for **gym** membership for **3 months**?

b) How much money could she save **each month** by getting the **combined** membership rather than the two **separate** memberships?

Q2 Rick is investigating how much fruit the people in his class eat.
He has drawn a tally chart to show his results.

Pieces of fruit eaten each day	Tally	Frequency
0	卌	
1	卌 |||	
2						
3	卌 卌	
4				
5			

a) Copy and complete Rick's tally chart.

b) How many people did Rick ask?

c) What is the **modal number** of pieces of fruit eaten by people in Rick's class?

Health and Fitness

Q3 Ribble Rovers and Duddon Dragons play in the Furnish Netball League.
Their results from this season so far are shown below.

Ribble Rovers

Result	No. of games this season
Won	12
Lost	5
Drawn	2

Duddon Dragons

Result	No. of games this season
Won	13
Lost	4
Drawn	2

Scoring Rules:
Win — 3 points
Draw — 1 point
Lose — 0 points

a) How many **points** does each team have?

b) In the final match of the season, Ribble Rovers beat Duddon Dragons.
How many points will each team finish the season with?

Q4 Fred is choosing the player of the month for his cricket team.
He looks at the number of runs three players scored in their last three matches.

Match 1

Cricketer	Runs
Mark	59
Ryan	56
Peter	72

Match 2

Cricketer	Runs
Mark	42
Ryan	50
Peter	41

Match 3

Cricketer	Runs
Mark	38
Ryan	42
Peter	49

a) Which player scored the most runs **in total**?

b) Which player has the highest **mean** score?

Health and Fitness

Q5 Jane works at Local Leisure Ltd. She wants to improve the centre. She is making a questionnaire to find out what people like about the centre and what they don't like.

> 1. How often do you come to Local Leisure Ltd?
>
> 2. Which leisure facilities do you use here?
>
> 3. What other facilities would you like us to offer?

a) Jane decides to give people a **choice** of answers to pick from.
Suggest **four** choices she could give people for **Q1**.

b) How could Jane make sure **as many members as possible** get a copy of the questionnaire?

c) What could Jane do to **encourage** members to **fill in** and **return** the questionnaire?

Q6 Steve has done a 10 km run. He used a stopwatch to record his time for each kilometre. He's plotted his times on the line graph below.

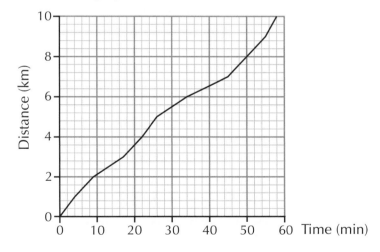

a) How long did it take Steve to run the **whole race**?

b) Steve thinks that the **first 5 km** took him **longer** than the **second 5 km**. Is he right?

54

Health and Fitness

Q7 Jane is making a display board for Local Leisure Ltd. She has collected information from members on how much they exercise and their Body Mass Index (BMI). She has put the information in a table and has started to make a graph.

Hours of exercise per week	10	9	8	7	12	8	6	9	9	8
BMI	20	21	23	25	16	24	28	22	23	25

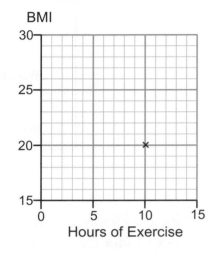

a) Copy and complete Jane's **scatter graph** of BMI against number of hours of exercise.

b) What **relationship** does the graph show between BMI and time spent exercising?

Q8 Clive is trying to lose weight. His personal trainer told him to keep a food diary for one week. Clive's diary is shown below.

Clive's Food Diary
Mon   2700 cals
Tues   2550 cals
Weds   2450 cals
Thurs 2650 cals
Fri   2500 cals
Sat   2750 cals
Sun   2950 cals

Notes...
Only need 2500 cals per day to stay at the same weight.

a) Calculate the **mean** number of calories that Clive eats each day.

b) How many **fewer** calories should Clive eat **each week** to maintain his current weight?

Health and Fitness

Car Boot Sale

Q1   Sarah has set up a stall at a car boot sale. Some items that she is selling are shown below.

All books and CDs 80p

All soft toys £1.30

£2.50

£1.20

a)   A customer buys **two CDs**. How much should Sarah charge her?

b)   Another customer buys a **book** and a **teddy bear**. How much should Sarah charge him?

c)   A third customer buys a **book**, a **CD**, a **hairdryer** and a **scarf**.
How much should Sarah charge him?

Q2   Nick is also selling at the car boot sale. Some of his items are shown below.

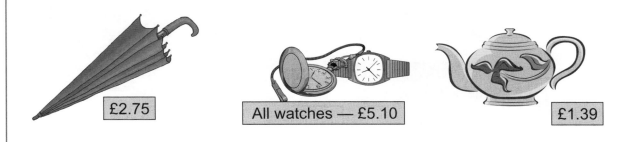

£2.75

All watches — £5.10

£1.39

a)   A customer buys an **umbrella** and a **watch**. He pays with a **£10** note.
How much **change** should Nick give him?

b)   Another customer buys a **teapot** and a **watch**. He gives Nick **£7**.
How much **change** should he get?

Car Boot Sale

Q3 Kelsie is selling at a car boot sale. She has written up a price list.

Kelsie's Bargain Boot Sale

Prices

Gloves: £1.73   Bracelets: 79p   DVDs: £1.27

Toaster: £2.45   Leg Warmers: £1.43   Play-pen: £7.99

Towards the end of the day Kelsie runs out of change. She decides to round all her prices to the **nearest 10p**. What price should she charge for **each item**?

Q4 Dave wants to buy some cushions. He visits two different stalls.

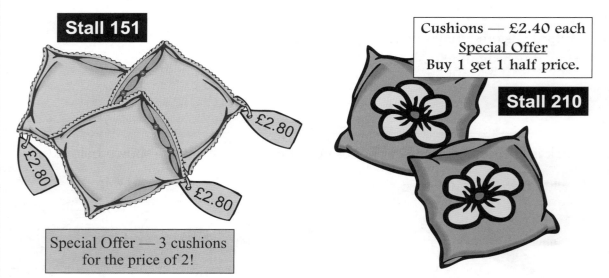

Stall 151

£2.80   £2.80   £2.80

Special Offer — 3 cushions for the price of 2!

Cushions — £2.40 each
Special Offer
Buy 1 get 1 half price.

Stall 210

a) How much would it cost Dave to buy **three cushions** from stall 151?

b) How much would it cost Dave to buy **three cushions** from stall 210?

c) Dave buys three cushions from the stall where they are **cheapest**.
He pays with a £20 note and is given **£12.60** change. Is this the right amount?

Car Boot Sale

Q5 Chris packs the all items he wants to sell into boxes and crates, shown below.

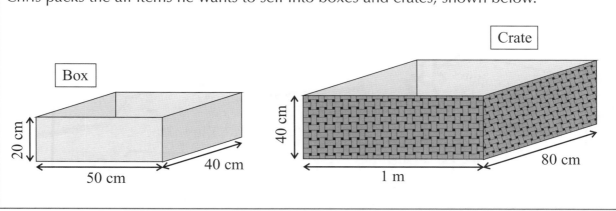

a) What is the **volume** of each **box**?

b) What is the **volume** of each **crate**?

c) How many **boxes** will Chris be able to pack into **each crate**?

Q6 Jonny has £8 to spend. He sees some things he wants to buy, shown below.

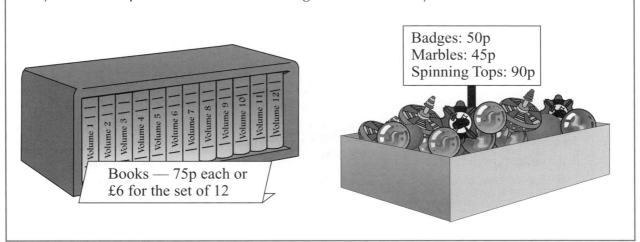

Badges: 50p
Marbles: 45p
Spinning Tops: 90p

Books — 75p each or £6 for the set of 12

a) Jonny already has **three books** from the set.
Is it cheaper for him to buy **only** the books that he **needs** or to buy the **whole set**?

b) Jonny decides to spend the rest of his money on **marbles**.
How many can he afford to buy?

Car Boot Sale

Q7 Melanie thinks that the prices she is charging, shown below, may be too high.

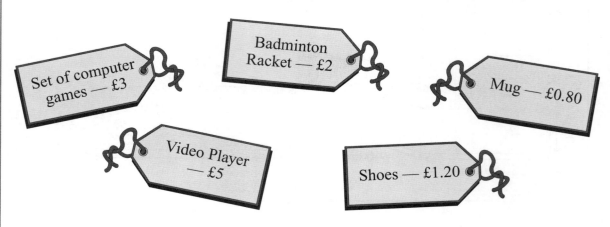

Set of computer games — £3

Badminton Racket — £2

Mug — £0.80

Video Player — £5

Shoes — £1.20

a) Melanie decides to **reduce** everything by **15%**.
How much money will she reduce **each item** by?

b) What **prices** should Melanie write on each of the labels?

Q8 Jess has made **15 bead necklaces** to sell.
The receipts for the materials she bought to make the necklaces are shown below:

necklace clasps	£11.25
thin leather cord	£3.80
Total	£15.05

Glass beads (large) — £9.65	
Glass beads (small) — £6.10	
Total — £15.75	

large red beads	£4.00
small blue beads	£1.60
small red beads	£1.60
painted beads	£2.50
Total	£9.70

a) How much did it cost Jess to **buy** the materials?

b) Jess wants to make a **20% profit**. What price will she need to sell **each** necklace for?

Banking

Q1 Mrs Hammond has just become a grandmother to triplets.
She decides to save some money for them to share when they turn 18.

> To Harry, Heidi & Harvey.
>
> I have opened an account with £300,
> and every year on your birthday will
> add another £100.
> After your 18th birthday you can
> split the money equally between you.
>
> Lots of love, Grandma xxx

a) How much money will be in the account after the triplets' **18th birthday**?

b) How much money will **each** of the triplets get when they split it equally at age 18?

Q2 Matthew gets paid his student loan twice a year.
He has to make the money last **6 months**.

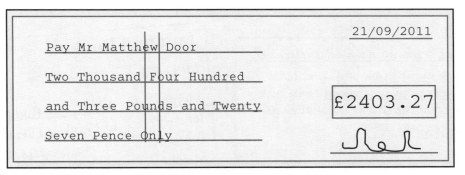

21/09/2011

Pay Mr Matthew Door

Two Thousand Four Hundred

and Three Pounds and Twenty

Seven Pence Only

£2403.27

a) Estimate how much Matthew can spend **each month**.

b) After 3 months his bank balance is **£897.94**.
Estimate how much he can spend each month in the **next 3 months**.

c) In his final year at university, Matthew gets a **10% increase** in his payments.
Approximately how much will he be able to spend each month after the increase?

Banking

Q3 Dylan is a student looking to open a bank account. He has **£100** to pay in.
Two high street banks are offering the following deals:

PGS Bank

Open a student account with us today and we will give you **20%** of however much you pay in.

Lomond Bank

Students!
Looking for an account?

Look no further — at Lomond Bank we will give you a **quarter** of whatever you pay in to open your account!
(Up to a maximum payout of £30)

a) How much would **PGS** pay into Dylan's account, if he opened an account with them?

b) Which bank offers the best deal for Dylan?

Q4 Dylan's dad is encouraging him to save money in his new account.
In January he made him an offer to help him along.

Dylan's 6 Month Saving Challenge!
For each month you pay in at least £20 more than you spend I will give you £10 at the end of the challenge.

Good luck!
Dad x

Lomond Bank

Mr D Roberts

Month	Paid In	Paid Out
January	£125.00	£96.73
February	£93.45	£52.02
March	£87.60	£69.43
April	£52.85	£36.98
May	£99.76	£48.50
June	£74.50	£106.32

a) In **which months** did Dylan meet his dad's target?

b) **How much money** should Dylan get from his dad at the end of June?

Banking

Q5 Sean earns **£20 000** per year, and has **£10 000** saved up for a deposit on a new flat.
He has received a letter from his bank about taking out a mortgage.

> ## PGS Bank
>
> Dear Mr Bourne
>
> I can confirm that we can lend you up to **2½ times** your salary as a mortgage.
>
> You will need to pay at least **one fifth** of the value of the property as a deposit.
>
> Please make an appointment to see one of our advisors to discuss this further.
>
> Yours sincerely
>
> _Dan Le Maison_
>
> PGS Mortgages

a) How much money will the bank lend to Sean based on his present salary?

b) Sean has seen a flat for sale for **£55 000**.
How much more money does he need to save as a deposit for this flat?

Q6 Sean decides to wait until he has saved **£1500** more before he buys a flat.
He starts to pay a fixed amount each month into a savings account, as shown below.

> **PGS Online Banking**
>
> Standing Order - Step 3
> Fill out the details below.
>
> | Date of First Payment: | 1st March |
> | Frequency: | Monthly |
> | Amount: | £120 |
>
> Confirm Standing Order

a) **How long** will it take Sean to save £1500, if the only money
paid into the account is his monthly standing order?

b) Sean decides this is too long to wait. He wants to save £1500 in **6 months**.
How much will Sean need to save each month to do this?

Banking

Q7   Rebekkah's mum has won some money.
She puts **£2000** in a savings account for her daughter.

> ### Sharkley's Building Society
>
> <u>Savings Account Terms and Conditions</u>
>
> Interest on this account will be paid every 12 months.
>
> Interest will be added to the account at a rate of **<u>4%</u>** of the total amount in the account.
>
> No money can be withdrawn without closing the account.

a)   How much money can Rebekkah expect to be in the savings account after **one year**?

b)   Rebekkah decides to leave the money in the account until she leaves school in two years' time. How much will she have in the account after **two years**?

Q8   Emily takes out a loan to buy the car shown below.
She wants to pay it back in full, plus interest, in **12 equal monthly** instalments.

Annual interest rates for loans

Amount Borrowed	Interest Rate
less than £5000	17%
£5000 - £10 000	15%
more than £10 000	13%

<u>How we work out your repayments</u>:
We add the interest amount to the amount you are borrowing and then split this total amount into equal monthly repayments.

a)   How much, **in total**, will Emily have to pay back to the bank?

b)   How much will Emily have to pay **each month**, to the nearest penny?

MFBW41